This Annual belongs to
Princess.............................

Art Editor: Alexandra Brown
Editor: Sally Gilbert
Photography: Colin Bowling

My

Disney's

Princess

Annual 2003

The A to Z of being a princess

Disney's Princess invites

(your name)

into a magical world, where you can discover the A to Z secrets of your favourite Disney princesses...

Now turn the page to begin the fairy-tale...

is for accessories

Every true princess knows that accessories are essential to looking great. A few well chosen accessories will transform any outfit!

Shoes

As Cinderella knows only too well, a princess can never have too many shoes! Choose a style that is comfortable for you.

Perfume

Always remember a spritz of perfume. This adds a feminine finish to your overall image and leaves a lasting impression.

Finishing touches

Before you leave for the ball, make sure you complete your outfit by adding a few finishing touches. Accessories give a polished finish to any gown.

Items		I have	I need
Shoes 		☐	☐
Gloves		☐	☐
Hand bag		☐	☐
Purse		☐	☐
Fan		☐	☐
Perfume		☐	☐

B is for ballgown

Discover the secrets of your favourite princess ballgowns. Learn exactly what details are needed to create a sensational, show-stopping gown.

Cinderella

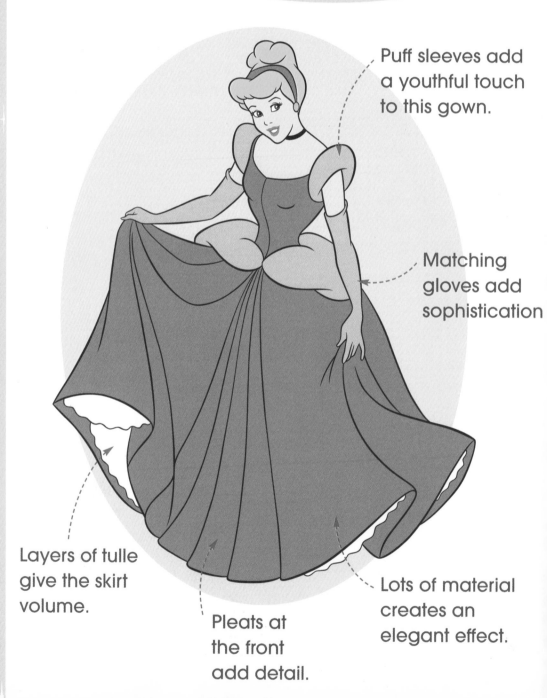

Puff sleeves add a youthful touch to this gown.

Matching gloves add sophistication

Layers of tulle give the skirt volume.

Pleats at the front add detail.

Lots of material creates an elegant effect.

Aurora

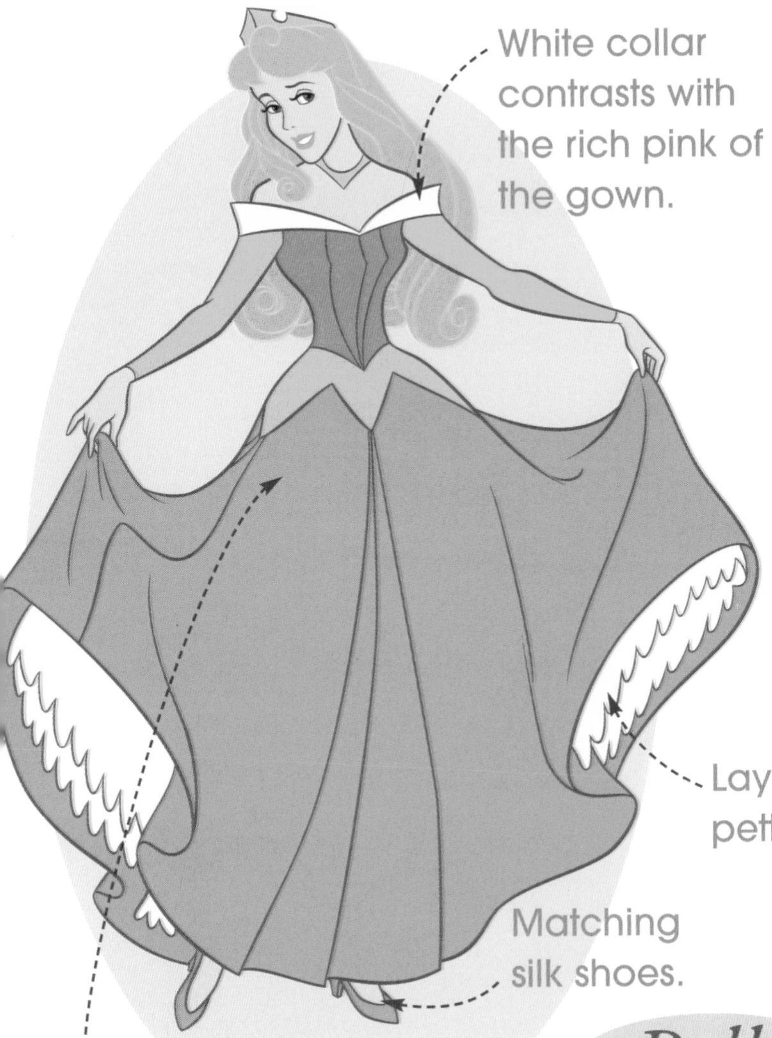

White collar contrasts with the rich pink of the gown.

Layers of silk petticoats.

Matching silk shoes.

Skirt falls from a drop waist.

Ballgown checklist

What details would your ballgown have?

Puff sleeves ☐

Off-the-shoulder ☐

Full skirt ☐

Silk petticoats ☐

Silk taffeta ☐

Matching shoes ☐

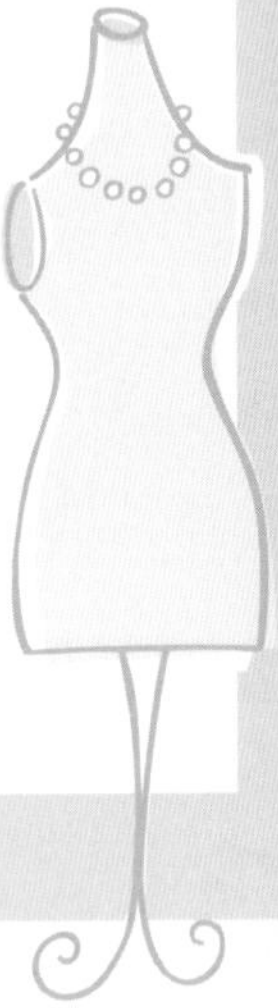

Belle

Glamorous off-the-shoulder neckline.

Ruched detail adds interest.

Hooped petticoats hold skirt in place.

Rich golden silk taffeta material.

7

is for castle

All princesses live in spectacular castles and palaces. Take our guided tour around their homes and discover magical princess worlds.

Ariel

Ariel's home is truly unique. Fashioned from sparkling coral, it shimmers through the waves. Inside it is just as stunning, with huge windows giving glorious views of the ocean.

Cinderella

Cinderella lives in a spectacular, golden-turreted palace. Towers soar into the sky and can be seen for miles around. The interior is extremely luxurious, with rich fabrics and glittering mirrors.

Belle

Belle lives deep in the countryside, amongst acres of green forest. Her home is a pretty, fairy-tale castle, with beautiful gothic style towers. Inside, the centre-piece is a beautiful ballroom, where Belle loves to dance.

Jasmine

Jasmine's home is fantastic. The golden walls shimmer in the desert heat and the exotic towers glint in the sun. Inside it is cool and peaceful, with opulent furnishings in every room.

Aurora

Aurora resides in a perfect, hill top palace, surrounded by rolling countryside. It is topped by pretty pink towers. Inside, Aurora has brought her own stylish touch to what was a rather cold, medieval home.

9

 *is for dressing-up*

Princesses love to dress up!
Follow our simple guide and you too
can look like a fairy-tale princess in
no time at all!

Dressing-up tips

You can use any clothes and items you have at
home to create your own stunning look.

 Adapt old party
or bridesmaid
dresses.

 Create glamorous
shawls from old
pieces of material.

 Add glamour to
old clothes by
gluing on sequins
and glitter.

 Add accessories
to a simple outfit -
a feather boa or
sparkly shoes.

 Ask if you can
borrow things
from older
relatives.

 A tiara is
essential - you
can make or
buy one.

 Keep everything
tidy in a dressing-
up box or drawer.

Belle

Pretty rose covered tiara or head-dress.

Silk ribbon can be used as a necklace.

Sarong tied to form a pretty wrap.

Lacy petticoat can be used as a long skirt.

Follow these easy tips and transform yourself into beautiful Belle.

Mulan

Use chopsticks as hair accessories.

Create a Mulan hairstyle.

Silky nightshirt can become a Mulan kimono.

These simple tips will help you become an elegant princess, just like Mulan.

11

is for enchantment

A princess's world is full of enchantment and magic. It comes in many forms and always helps a princess to enjoy life to the full.

Magic Carpet

Jasmine is lucky enough to have all the fantastic magic of the Genie and the Magic Carpet at her disposal.

Fairy Princess

Tinkerbell is not only a princess, but she also possesses magical fairy powers herself.

Fairy Godmother

With a wave of her Fairy Godmother's magic wand, Cinderella has everything she needs to attend the ball.

Good Fairies

Aurora's fairy friends, Flora, Fauna and Merryweather use their magic to give her joy and happiness.

Princess Spell

• • • • • • • • • • • • • • • • •

For this princess spell
(You know only too well)
That an absolute must
Is a touch of magic dust,
Mixed with a drop of pure love,
A star from above,
And a splash of happiness
From a true princess.

• • • • • • • • • • • • • • • • •

F is for friendship

True friendship is very important to all princesses. Read our friendship tips to become a better friend.

Ocean friends

Princess Ariel has lots of friends, each of them different. Scuttle the seagull is her trusted consultant on all things human. Flounder the fish is her playtime friend.

Enchanted friends

Belle was without any real friends in her village. But at the Beast's castle she finds true companionship with the enchanted objects: Lumiere, Cogsworth, Mrs Potts and her son, Chip.

Magical friends

Mulan has her dog, Little Brother, and her horse, Khan, as friends, but her closest companion is Mushu, the little dragon. Not only is he a friend, he is her guardian, sent by Mulan's ancestors to protect her.

Friendship tips

- Always be ready to listen to a friend's problems.

- Be kind when friends are upset about something.

- Remember your friends' birthdays.

- Spend quality time together.

- Share your belongings with your friends.

- Take up a hobby with your friends and have fun.

Forest friends

The animals who live in the forest near the cottage are Aurora's friends. The princess tells them all about her dreams and they're the ones who make the meeting between her and Prince Phillip possible.

Wild friends

Jasmine's pet tiger, Rajah, accompanies her on many adventures and is fiercely protective of his royal mistress. Jasmine is the only person who can cuddle Rajah!

is for glitter

Glitter and sparkle - that's what princesses are made of. Sprinkle a little glitter and add some sparkle to your life, too.

Glitter bracelet

Make this bracelet - it will add a princess sparkle to any outfit!

You will need:

Cuff bracelet
Glitter
Non-toxic glue
Jewels

1 Make sure the bracelet is clean and dry. Then cover completely in glue.

2 Stick jewels on to the bracelet in whatever pattern you wish.

3 Cover the bracelet with glitter and allow to dry, then shake off excess glitter.

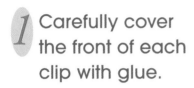

Glitter hair-clips

You'll glitter like a princess when
you make these sparkly hair-clips!

1 Carefully cover
the front of each
clip with glue.

2 Sprinkle each clip
with glitter and
allow to dry.

3 Shake off the excess
glitter and add sparkle
to your hairstyle!

You will need:

Hair-clips

Glitter

Non-toxic glue

Sparkle Secrets

 For a party or special
occasion, sprinkle a
little glitter in your hair
gel and see the results.

 Add a touch of glamour
to your princess
wardrobe by investing in
a few glittery outfits.

 Glitter make-up is
everywhere this season,
so have some fun and
shine like a star.

 When it comes to
applying glitter,
always remember that
less is definitely more.

H is for happiness

Most princesses live happily ever after. Discover what makes each of these princesses truly happy.

Ariel

Happiness checklist

Adventures	✓	Friends	✓
Cooking		Parties	
Dancing		Reading	
Dressing-up		Romance	✓
Flowers	✓	Singing	✓
Flying		Swimming	✓

Snow White

Happiness checklist

Adventures		Friends	✓
Cooking	✓	Parties	
Dancing	✓	Reading	
Dressing-up	✓	Romance	✓
Flowers	✓	Singing	✓
Flying		Swimming	

Jasmine

Happiness checklist

Adventures	✓	Flowers	✓	Reading	☐
Cooking	☐	Flying	✓	Romance	✓
Dancing	✓	Friends	✓	Singing	☐
Dressing-up	✓	Parties	✓	Swimming	☐

Belle

Happiness checklist

Adventures	☐	Friends	✓
Cooking	☐	Parties	✓
Dancing	✓	Reading	✓
Dressing-up	✓	Romance	✓
Flowers	✓	Singing	☐
Flying	☐	Swimming	☐

My happiness checklist

Tick the things that make you happy and add some of your own.

Adventures	✓	Flowers	✓	Reading	✓	Dane mat	✓
Cooking	✓	Flying	✓	Romance	✓	....	☐
Dancing	✓	Friends	✓	Singing	✓	....	☐
Dressing-up	✓	Parties	✓	Swimming	✓		

is for imagination

Princesses have very vivid imaginations. They imagine what they could be doing, and who they could be meeting - and luckily for them, dreams really do come true!

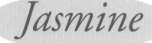
Cinderella

Although Cinderella lives with her cruel stepmother and stepsisters, she never stops dreaming that a life filled with kindness and love awaits her.

Jasmine

Jasmine often dreams of exciting adventures, away from the confines of her father's palace.

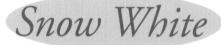
Snow White

Snow White dreams of the day her prince will come and sweep her off her feet - and one day he does!

Your imagination

In the space below, use your imagination and draw
your very own princess world.

The meaning of dreams

Discover the true meanings of your dreams. If
you dream of...

An adventure

You need speed
and excitement

A romance

You will have
happiness and fun

A castle

You can expect a
comfortable future

Being a princess

You can expect love
and admiration

Friends

You will have
happy times

Happiness

There are good
times ahead

J is for jewels

Princesses cherish their jewels and gemstones as they believe them to have special powers. Discover these princesses' perfect treasures.

Turquoise

Turquoise would be the perfect jewel for Jasmine, as it would protect her from harm whenever she goes on her exciting adventures with Aladdin.

Emerald

An emerald jewel would suit Aurora, because she could carry it whenever she left the palace and it would ward off evil forces and give her special powers.

Ruby

Ruby would be the perfect jewel for Belle, as it would enhance her spiritual wisdom and positive energy.

Aquamarine

Sapphire

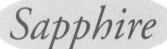

Sapphire would be the ultimate jewel for Cinderella, as it could give her the strength and protection to overcome her wicked stepmother.

Aquamarine would be perfect for Ariel, as it would protect her from the perils of the ocean, and give her a little direction in life, too.

Birth Stones

Find out what your birth stone is:

January - Garnet	May - Emerald	September - Sapphire
February - Amethyst	June - Pearl	October - Opal
March - Aquamarine	July - Ruby	November - Topaz
April - Diamond	August - Peridot	December - Turquoise

23

_K_ is for kingdom

According to fairy-tales, princesses live in wonderful kingdoms far, far away. Discover the worlds where some of your favourite Disney princesses live.

Jasmine

Kingdom	Kingdom of Agrabah
Ruler	Sultan of Agrabah
Description	A kingdom mostly made up of desert land, but very rich in natural resources. Agrabah is a rich, shimmering, desert oasis.

Aurora

Kingdom	Woodland kingdom
Inhabitants	Woodland animals
Description	A kingdom of pretty countryside, with thick forests, perfect for hunting, riding and walking.

Cinderella

Kingdom	Fairy-tale kingdom
Ruler	The King
Description	The ultimate princess kingdom, overlooked by a fantastic fairy-tale palace which is surrounded by pretty countryside.

Ariel

Kingdom	Underwater kingdom
Ruler	King Triton
Description	A unique, stunning underwater kingdom, filled with colourful sea-flowers that stretch as far as the eye can see.

Belle

Kingdom	Enchanted kingdom
Inhabitants	Enchanted objects and the Beast
Description	A small, but beautiful enchanted kingdom. It is a green and fertile land, with lovely lakes and secret islands.

L is for letters

All princesses love to send and receive letters. Make your own personal stationery and leave a lasting impression.

Letter Tips

- Always use your neatest hand writing.
- Try to reply to letters promptly.
- Send 'thank you' letters for any gifts.
- Keep all your letters in a special 'letter box'.

Scroll letter

Add a regal touch to any letter!

1. This is a very simple way of giving your letters a princess touch. Just roll a piece of paper into a scroll and secure by tying with a pretty ribbon.

You will need:
Paper
Silky ribbon

Personal stationery

Make your very own stylish
personalised stationery!

You will need:

Cartridge paper

Half a large potato

Poster paints

Craft knife

1 With the help of an adult, carefully mark a shape on the potato, a star for example. Cut away the potato around your shape.

2 Dip the potato into your paint and stamp on to the paper. Leave to dry. You can create any design you wish.

Princess Tip
Try decorating matching envelopes, too.

M is for make-up

Every princess loves to experiment with make-up. Read the essential beauty tips every glamorous girl should know.

Natural beauty

Your best make-up is your smile. Princesses wear make-up to enhance their features, not to cover up their natural beauty.

Lipstick

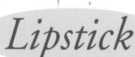

Your lipstick colour should compliment your gown. Just a hint of a pretty pink, or some clear lipgloss will look beautiful.

Nails

Make sure your nails are clean, neat and tidy. Clean, buffed nails look great for everyday - leave the bright colours for parties.

Hair

Clean, well-groomed hair is another princess essential. Brush your hair until it shines and add pretty hair accessories.

Face

Fresh, clean skin is a must for a princess. Save sparkly make-up for parties and always remember to remove any make-up before you go to bed.

Princess make-over

Try this simple Cinderella look. Twist your hair into a bun on the top of your head and secure with hair pins. Add a pretty hairband. A touch of lipgloss finishes this pretty make-over.

29

Princess Bedrooms

On the following pages, discover the secrets of your favourite princesses' bedrooms.

Ariel

Ariel's bedroom is decorated in pretty pastel colours that work with the aquamarine ocean surrounding the palace. She has a stunning four-poster bed, fashioned from coral.

Aurora

Aurora's bedroom is luxurious and old fashioned. Her bed covers are made from the finest silks and her pillow cases the softest satin. No wonder she managed to sleep for 100 years!

Jasmine

Jasmine's bedroom has an exotic influence. The room is covered with satin and sheer material drapes and the fabrics are rich. There are lots of different shaped pillows scattered everywhere.

Belle

Belle's bedroom is very special indeed. Not only is it very pretty, it is wonderfully enchanted. Belle has lots of fun, because Mrs Wardrobe helps her decide which ballgown to wear each day.

Mulan

Mulan's bedroom has a strong oriental feel. It is simple, yet elegant. There is an air of calm and relaxation to this room, because of the soothing colours that have been used.

Princess Dream Bedroom

Read how to transform your bedroom into a 'Princess Dream Bedroom' and then enter our fantastic competition.

Make a crown from card and position it above the bed.

Tie back your curtains with pretty ribbon.

Drape floaty material from the crown.

Decorate a wardrobe with bright colours.

Attach silk flowers to the head-board.

Keep all your princess dresses together.

Put a silky throw over the bed.

Decorate the room in pretty pastel colours.

Attach silk flowers to the end of the bed.

Keep the room clean and tidy.

Competition Time!

Dear Readers,

In addition to the opportunity to win a break at Disneyland Paris, we've got some rather special Princess prizes, courtesy of Vivid Imaginations, to give away, in this very easy to enter competition.

Enter the magical world of Disney's Princess ...

where you can wish upon a star and be whisked away to Cinderella's Magical Musical Castle. Each room within the castle reveals spellbinding lights and sound effects to recreate the magic of Disney.

We have five Cinderella Magical Musical Castles to be won.
(RRP £29.99 each)

 Five Winners! If you are a runner-up, you can watch Cinderella transform from her simple maid's rags into the belle of the ball in this set of two outfits, complete with miniature blue birds and dazzling ball gown.

We have five Cinderella Rags to Riches Dolls to be won.(RRP £14.99 each)

Five Runners-up!

 # How to enter

All you have to do is **design your own Princess Dream Bedroom** (don't forget to put your name, address and age on the back) and post it to:

Princess Dream Bedroom Competition, Egmont Books Limited, Unit 7, Millbank House, Riverside Park, Wilmslow, Cheshire, SK9 1BJ. The closing date is 27th January 2003.

Rules
1. 10 Winners will be chosen at random and notified by post.
2. Judges' decision will be final. No correspondence will be entered into.
3. The winners' names will be made available from Egmont Books Limited (on request) after 5th February 2003. Please enclose a stamped addressed envelope for reply.
4. Employees (and their relatives) of Egmont Books Limited and their associated companies are not eligible to enter.
5. Entries are limited to one per person, and cannot be returned.
6. Competition is open to residents of the UK, Channel Islands and Ireland only.
7. The publishers reserve the right to vary prizes subject to availability.
8. Closing date for entries is 27th January 2003.

is for nature

All princesses love to be close to nature. They spend time outdoors whenever they can, and many of their friends are woodland creatures.

Belle

Belle loves to relax in the grounds of the Beast's castle. She likes to sit in the sun reading, and organises wonderful outdoor picnics.

Ariel

Ariel is very close to nature, exploring the oceans that form her father's kingdom. Her best friends are sea-creatures and she loves to dress her hair with the natural beauty of sea-flowers.

34

Snow White

It was the woodland creatures who first discovered Snow White, deep in the woods. Since then she has felt very close to her woodland friends.

Aurora

Aurora may be a princess, but she is a natural girl at heart. She loves nothing better than spending her time in the forest, surrounded by her woodland friends.

Symbols in nature

 Four-leaf clover
Good luck

 Shell
Good luck

 **Sea horse**
Constancy

 Red rose
True love

 Forget-me-not
Good luck

 Daffodil
Happiness

 Butterfly
New life

 Daisy
Friendship

 Primrose
Good luck

is for once upon a time

Most princesses have their very own fairy-tale story. Read Princess Aurora's enchanting tale entitled 'Sleeping Beauty'.

Once upon a time, a beautiful baby was born to a good king and a gentle queen. Overjoyed, the king and queen named their daughter **Aurora**, which means "dawn", because she brightened their lives with happiness just as the sun brightens the day.

The three good fairies came to bestow gifts on the new princess. The first fairy, **Flora**, gave the princess the gift of beauty. The second fairy, **Fauna**, gave her the gift of song. As the third fairy flew over to the baby's cradle, the wicked fairy, **Malificent**,

suddenly appeared. Angry that she had not been invited to the celebration she pu a curse on the princess: *By the end of her sixteent birthday, Aurora wil. prick her finger on a spindle...and die!*

The third good fairy, **Merryweather**, used her gift to weaken Malificent's curse. The princess would not die upon pricking her finger but would fall into a deep sleep, to be awakened by true love's first kiss.

Even with **Merryweather's** help, the king still feared for his daughter's life. To prevent the evil curse from coming true, he ordered every spinning wheel in the kingdom to be burned.

But Flora came up with a better idea to protect Aurora from Malificent. The three good fairies took the baby princess to a cottage in the woods where they raised her as their own daughter. They called her Briar Rose. Under the care of the fairies, she grew to be sweet and lovely. On her sixteenth birthday, she was sitting in the forest, singing, when a prince from a nearby kingdom overheard her. Prince Phillip and Briar Rose quickly fell in love.

But it was time for Briar Rose to return to her parents and learn that she was really Princess Aurora. The three good fairies led her back to the palace.

At the palace, Aurora followed a strange light up a secret staircase. In a small room at the top of the stairs, she found a spinning wheel that Malificent had put there. When Aurora reached out to touch the spindle, she pricked her finger and fell into a deep sleep.

The three good fairies knew that the king and queen would be heart-broken when they discovered Aurora. So they flew about the palace putting everyone else into a deep sleep.

Then, they armed Prince Phillip with a magic sword and shield so he could fight Malificent. The evil fairy turned herself into a fierce dragon, but Prince Phillip threw his sword at her and pierced her cold heart.

Prince Phillip then ran through the palace gates and up to the chamber where Aurora lay. He knelt beside the princess and kissed her gently on the lips. The sleeping beauty awakened and smiled at her prince.

Then everyone in the kingdom awoke. The princess and her parents rushed joyfully into each other's arms, reunited at last.

Soon after, Prince Aurora and Prince Phillip were married and everyone lived happily ever after.

The End

is for prince

You are familiar with your favourite princesses, but what about their princes? You can read all about them here.

Prince Charming

Royal Fact File

Colour of eyes	Brown
Colour of hair	Brown
Status	Royal prince
Likes	Riding and dancing
True love	Cinderella

Prince Aladdin

Royal Fact File

Colour of eyes	Brown
Colour of hair	Black
Status	Commoner
Likes	Adventure and flying
True love	Jasmine

Prince Charming

Prince Phillip

Royal Fact File

Colour of eyes	Blue
Colour of hair	Auburn
Status	Royal prince
Likes	Riding and hunting
True love	Snow White

Royal Fact File

Colour of eyes	Dark brown
Colour of hair	Light brown
Status	Royal prince
Likes	Riding and dancing
True love	Aurora

Prince Eric

Royal Fact File

Colour of eyes	Blue
Colour of hair	Black
Status	Royal prince
Likes	Sailing and adventure
True love	Ariel

is for quiz

Complete our quiz to see which princess you are most like. Just circle one answer for each question and see which letter you score most of.

 Questions

1) Your hair is closest to...

a) Dark and curly

b) Blonde

c) Brown

d) Black and straight

e) Golden blonde

f) Red

2) Your style might be called

a) Exotic

b) Glamorous

c) Party princess

d) Elegant

e) Traditional

f) Beachwear

3) Your ideal pet is a...

a) Tiger

b) Mouse

c) You are not fond of animals

d) Horse

e) Owl

f) Fish

4) Your favourite hobby is...

a) Adventure

b) Organising parties

c) Reading

d) Dancing

e) Walking

f) Collecting things

5) Where would you prefer to live?

a) In the desert

b) In a palace

c) In a castle

d) Your family home

e) In a secluded cottage

f) By the ocean

Mostly a

You're like Jasmine

You are an exotic beauty who enchants everyone you meet. You love going on wonderful adventures and have a special fondness for tigers.

Mostly b

You're like Cinderella

You are a true party girl. You love dressing up in glamorous outfits and holding parties. You are also very kind and caring.

Mostly c

You're like Belle

You are loving and giving and can always see the good in others. You love to read and spend time with friends.

Mostly d

You're like Mulan

You have a strong sense of family values and always strive for their approval. You have a special love of music, dance and riding.

Mostly e

You're like Aurora

You love all woodland animals, especially owls. You like dreaming, but be careful you don't sleep away your life waiting for true love's first kiss!

Mostly f

You're like Ariel

You are totally in love with the sea and really enjoy collecting its treasures. Everyone finds your youthfulness very attractive.

R is for romance

Read how the great romances of your favourite princesses and their princes really started.

Jasmine

Jasmine decided to make her own decision as to which young man she would spend the rest of her life with. The young man was Aladdin, and not a prince.

Belle

Belle is very romantic. Gaston's appearance and boastings were certainly not enough to win her heart. Belle needs to be understood and to share her world with the man she loves.

Cinderella

Cinderella falls in love with Prince Charming the moment she lays eyes on him. For one magic night, she dances with a handsome stranger, never knowing he's the prince himself.

Ariel

So that Ariel can live on land and be close to Prince Eric, she agrees to sign a very dangerous deal with the sea-witch, putting herself at great risk.

Aurora

Aurora dreamed of Prince Phillip for years. When they met, he was as wonderful as she had always imagined him to be. For his part, it only took that one encounter to inspire him to take on Malificent and save Aurora.

43

is for song

All princesses love to sing about their
dreams, hopes and happy endings.
Now you can, too.

Snow White

Snow White has the
voice of an angel.
She can even charm
the birds from the
trees. She loves to
sing about meeting
her prince.

Ariel

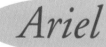

Ariel has an
extraordinary singing
voice. People say it is
as clear and as
beautiful as a bell.

A princess love song

The whole world changes when you're in love,
Your heart starts singing,
You're as high as a dove,
You're giddy with dreaming - oh, when you're in love.

The whole world changes when you're in love,
Sweet music awaits you,
Stars smile down from above,
Dreams do come true - oh, when you're in love.

The whole world changes when you're in love,
You're under love's spell,
When you're with your true love,
You have magic on your mind - oh, when you're in love.

Write your own song

In the space below, create your own princess song.

T is for tiara

A tiara is the essential accessory for every princess! They come in all shapes and styles, and here's how to make one for yourself.

Aurora

Aurora is never seen without her beautiful tiara. Fashioned from solid gold, its delicate design sets off Aurora's tumbling golden curls.

Jasmine

Jasmine's tiara is designed in a very traditional Arabic style. It is set in the centre with an enormous blue, precious stone, that almost glows. As befits a princess, Jasmine has a tiara to match every outfit!

 # Golden tiara

Make this golden tiara - it's perfect
for a princess like you.

You will need:
- Gold paper
- Safety scissors
- Alice band
- Sticky tape
- Pencil

Tiara Tip
Make a tiara from silver paper, too!

1 Ask a grown-up to help you cut out a tiara shape from sparkly gold paper.

2 Draw a decorative pattern on your tiara and cut out the segments.

3 Tape the tiara shape to an Alice band.

4 Gently place on your head and wear with pride.

is for unique

All princesses have individual qualities that make them unique – read these descriptions and find out just what their special qualities are.

Ariel

Ariel's unique qualities are her insatiable desire for adventure and her willingness to help anyone in distress. Her helpful nature often gets her into trouble!

Belle

Belle's compassion towards everyone she encounters and her heart full of love, are qualities that are unique to her and make her a perfect princess.

Jasmine

Jasmine is a truly unique princess. She longs to escape the confines of her father's royal palace and enjoy adventures on the Magic Carpet with Aladdin.

Cinderella

The style and grace that Cinderella brings to everything she does is truly unique and her king-sized heart makes her the perfect princess.

 My unique qualities

In the space below, list your own unique qualities.

_____

_____

_____

_____

_____

_____

V is for villain

Where there are good princesses, there ar
always evil villains. They try desperately
to get the better of the princesses, but
good always triumphs in the end.

Stepsisters

Brown-haired Drizella
and red-headed
Anastasia are
Cinderella's wicked
stepsisters. They take
any opportunity to treat
Cinderella badly and
stand in her way.

Malificent

Malificent lives in a castle
on the Forbidden
Mountain, near Aurora's
palace. Her rage has no
limits. For her curses she
uses a staff to call forth the
forces of evil.

Ursula

Power hungry Ursula, the sea-witch, was driven from the underwater kingdom and she has longed to make King Triton and his daughters pay for it ever since.

Queen

Not only is the Queen a cruel stepmother, she is also a powerful and frightening witch. She is so obsessed with Snow White's beauty that she comes to hate her.

Jafar

Jafar is the sultan's cruel Vizier and he lives in the royal palace of Agrabah. He keeps Jasmine's father under his control with his hypnotic magic staff. He understands the dark side of magic and uses this to amass greater power.

W is for wedding

Royal weddings are a wonderful chance for everyone to dress up in their best clothes and celebrate the love story between a prince and princess!

Cinderella

Cinderella's wedding to Prince Charming was a truly romantic affair. The streets were lined with cheering crowds and Cinderella looked stunning in her full-skirted, off-the-shoulder, white gown and veil.

Ariel

Ariel and Prince Eric's wedding was a more intimate affair and a triumph of true love overcoming all the odds. Ariel's gown featured puff sleeves, a crinoline skirt and a veil secured with a sparkling tiara.

Attach an
Alice band to
tulle for
the veil.

Become a bride

These simple tips will help
you become a beautiful
dressing-up bride.

Attach
ribbons
to the
Alice band
for added
sparkle.

Stick sequins to
the veil for
added glitter.

Use an old party
dress for your
wedding dress.

Make a
bouquet
from any
flowers you
can find.

Put a petticoat
under the dress to
make it stand out.

Wedding Anniversaries

First	- Paper	Fifth	- Wood	Twenty fifth	- Silver
Second	- Cotton	Tenth	- Tin	Thirtieth	- Pearl
Third	- Linen	Fifteenth	- Crystal	Fortieth	- Ruby
Fourth	- Silk	Twentieth	- China	Fiftieth	- Gold

is for X factor

The X factors are the little things that add up to being a perfect princess.

Elegance

Elegance is an essential factor for a princess, and Mulan is the epitome of elegance. She always looks stylish and composed.

Charm

Charm is an important factor for a princess. Snow White charms everyone she meets with an innocence that is reflected in her gentle ways.

Natural beauty

Aurora is, like all princesses, a natural beauty. She is stunningly beautiful on the outside, but just as beautiful in the inside, too.

Kindness

Belle is tender-hearted and full of kindness. She will always help people, whatever the cost to herself. It is this kindness that transforms the Beast into a prince.

Independence

Ariel is a true princess with her independent character. This makes her headstrong and impulsive, always looking for adventure.

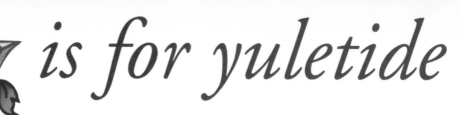

Y is for yuletide

Christmas is a time of year that all princesses enjoy. It's a time to have fun with friends and family.

Decorations

Princesses love to decorate their homes at Christmas with beautiful decorations. They also love wrapping up presents for their friends and family, making them as festive as possible.

Clothes

Yuletide is a great time of year for princesses, as it's a chance to wear new clothes. A beautiful yuletide gown is always top of a princess' Christmas list!

Having fun

Princesses love the Yuletide season, as it's a time to spend with friends and family, giving gifts, having fun, and enjoying the company of those you love.

Yuletide checklist

It's never too early to start preparing for Christmas!

	To do	Done
Gift list	☐	☐
Shopping list	☐	☐
Write cards	☐	☐
Send cards	☐	☐
Gifts for friends	☐	☐
Gifts for family	☐	☐

Z *is for zodiac*

Read our princess zodiac signs. Find out which princess you share a star sign with, and discover how similar you are!

Aquarius

21 January - 18 February

Like Pocahontas, you are an outdoor type and love to feel the wind in your hair. You are brave and strong.

Pisces

19 February - 20 March

Just like Ariel, you are headstrong and impetuous. You love having lots of fun but it often gets you into trouble.

Aries

21 March - 20 April

You have lots of friends, just like Esmeralda. People love to be around you and find you entertaining. You like to travel and visit new places.

Taurus

21 April - 21 May

You possess a certain magical quality, just like Tinkerbell. People often rely on you to make their dreams come true.

Gemini

22 May - 21 June

You and Cinderella could be twins! Your spirit, humour and dignity never falter. You are sweet-natured, kind and caring.

Cancer

22 June – 22 July

Like Aurora, you are a caring, loving and thoughtful girl. You make friends very easily as you are so kind and gentle.

Leo

23 July – 23 August

You are like lovely Snow White. You have a charming child-like innocence, which is reflected in your gentle ways and sweet nature.

Virgo

24 August – 22 September

You are just like Melody, you have the same happy-go-lucky nature. You are youthful and fun but sometimes a bit naive.

Libra

23 September – 23 October

You and Jasmine are just like two peas in a pod! You are a fiercely smart and independent individual. You love to feel free and explore the world.

Scorpio

24 October – 22 November

You are very quirky and lots of fun, just like Alice. You are inquisitive by nature and don't stop asking questions.

Sagittarius

23 November – 22 December

You are high-spirited and have lots of energy. Like Mulan, you are loyal to your friends and they adore you.

Capricorn

23 December – 20 January

You are very mature and extremely capable, just like Belle. You always do the right thing no matter what the cost.

Princess Quiz

Complete our quiz to find out if you are a true princess. The answers are on page 62.

1) What does Cinderella lose when she leaves the ball?

a) Her silk hand bag

b) Her glass slipper

c) Her diamond tiara

d) Her feather boa

2) Can you name the city Jasmine lives in?

a) Agrabah

b) Arabia

c) Ali baba

d) Agra

3) How long did Sleeping Beauty sleep for?

a) A year

b) Five years

c) 100 years

d) 1000 years

4) How many sisters does Ariel have?

a) None

b) One

c) Three

d) Six

5) How many dwarfs does Snow White live with?

a) Two

b) Six

c) Seven

d) Five

6) What is the name of Mulan's horse?

a) Khan

b) Chestnut

c) Dapple-grey

d) Little Brother

7) What is the enchanted flower the Beast keeps in the castle?

a) The enchanted daisy

b) The enchanted rose

c) The enchanted lily

d) The enchanted daffodil

8) What is the name of Pocahontas's raccoon friend?

a) Meeko

b) Meeka

c) Meku

d) Mekoo

Princess Quotations

Try and memorise these wonderful
princess quotations and use them each day.

"Once upon a time starts now..."
Cinderella

*"Dancing like I've never danced
before..."* *Cinderella*

*"A scent of roses. A dream of flying.
Love is in the air."* *Jasmine*

"Dreams come true." *Jasmine*

*"Can't stop smiling. Can't stop dancing.
Can't stop dreaming."* *Aurora*

"Dreaming of happily ever afters..."
Aurora

Princess Quiz
Answers

Find out how well you did in the
princess quiz on page 60.

Question 1) b

Question 2) a

Question 3) c

Question 4) d

Question 5) c

Question 6) a

Question 7) b

Question 8) a

Be a Princess!

Subscribe now and never miss an issue of Disney's Princess!

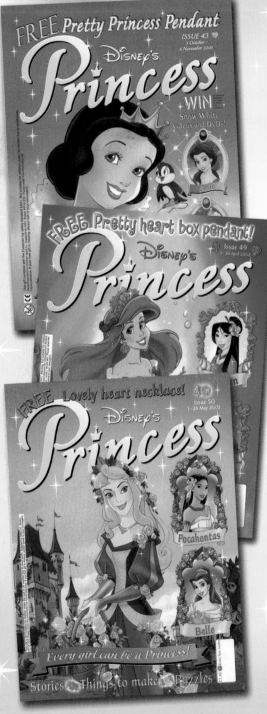

FREE Pretty Princess Pendant
ISSUE 43
3 October –
6 November 2001

Disney's **Princess**

WIN Snow White videos and DVDs!

FREE Pretty heart box pendant!
Issue 49
3 - 30 April 2002

Disney's **Princess**

FREE Lovely heart necklace!
Issue 50
1 - 28 May 2002

Disney's **Princess**

Pocahontas

Belle

Every girl can be a Princess!

Stories • Things to make • Puzzles

Egmont Magazines Subscriptions

Please note that, unless stated otherwise, the standard order period is twelve months and that new subscriptions take about four weeks to become effective. Sterling cheques and postal orders should be crossed and made payable to: **EGMONT MAGAZINES LIMITED**.

If you wish to pay by credit card or debit card, please remember to write your card number and expiry date in the spaces provided on the coupon and, if you are paying for someone else's subscription, you should add your own name and address in the separate space provided and send to: **Egmont Magazines Subscriptions, PO Box 315, Sittingbourne, Kent ME9 8DT**. Alternatively, call our credit card hotline on **01795 414 906** Cancelled subscriptions will be subject to a surcharge of 25% (twenty-five per cent) of the full subscriptions or £5.00, whichever is the higher, plus the cost of any issues despatched. Subscriptions cannot be cancelled after they have run for six months or more. Refunds can only be made to the person who paid for the subscription.

I wish to order a year's subscription (13 issues) to Disney's Princess as follows:

United Kingdom £18.85 ☐

I wish to order six months' subscription (7 issues) to Disney's Princess as follows:

United Kingdom £10.15 ☐

Subscriber:

FULL NAME .... (PAN2002)

ADDRESS ....

....

POSTCODE .... TELEPHONE ....

BIRTH DATE ....

Person Making Payment (If different from subscriber above)   Mr ☐   Mrs ☐   Ms ☐

FULL NAME ....

ADDRESS ....

....

POSTCODE .... TELEPHONE ....

I am the Parent/Brother/Sister/Aunt/Uncle/Grandparent/Friend/ .... of the subscriber

I enclose a crossed cheque/postal order for £....... made payable to **EGMONT MAGAZINES LIMITED** UK Bank or Eurocheque only

Please charge £.................... to my VISA/MASTERCARD/EUROCARD

Card Number ☐☐☐☐ ☐☐☐☐ ☐☐☐☐ ☐☐☐☐

Expiry Date ☐☐ ☐☐   Signature ☐☐☐☐☐☐☐

Please tick here ☐ if you do not want to receive notice of special offers or new products.

ORDERS & PAYMENTS TO:- Egmont Magazines Subscriptions, PO Box 315, Sittingbourne, Kent ME9 8DT. Tel: 01795 414 906 Subscription Expiry Date: 30/11/02

To ensure maximum quality of service we may occasionally monitor or record telephone calls made to 'Disney's Princess'

Instruction to your Bank or Building Society to pay by Direct Debit

DIRECT Debit

EGMONT

Please use a ball-point pen.

Originator's Identification Number ☐7☐6☐3☐9☐3☐9

Please fill in the whole form and send it to: Egmont Magazines Limited Subscriptions, PO Box 315, Sittingbourne, Kent ME9 8DT

1. Name and full postal address of your Bank or Building Society branch

To: The Manager .... Bank or Building Society

Address .... Postcode

2. Name(s) of Account Holder(s)

5. Reference number (For Office use only)

3. Branch Sort Code
(from the top right hand corner of your cheque)

☐☐ — ☐☐ — ☐☐

6. Instructions to your Bank or Building Society
Please pay Egmont Magazines Limited Direct Debits from the account detailed on this instruction subject to the safeguards assured by the Direct Debit Guarantee. I understand that this Instruction may remain with Egmont Magazines Limited and, if so, details will be passed electronically to my Bank/Building Society.

4. Bank/Building Society account number

☐☐☐☐☐☐☐☐

Signature(s)

Date

Banks and Building Societies may not accept Direct Debit Instructions for some type of accounts.

PAN2002